THE STORY OF GELERT

JOAN PERKINS

A long time ago in North Wales, there lived a Prince and a Princess.

The Princess was very beautiful. Her long hair was as fine as the finest golden silk. She washed it in the clear mountain water and brushed it a hundred times every night. Her eyes were as blue as the sky on a mid-summer day and her smile made everyone happy.

Prince Llewellyn was tall and strong and brave. He rode his horse better than any other man in the land and often hunted in the forests. But he was kind and gentle and loved the Princess very dearly. He was very proud and happy when the Princess presented him with a baby son.

The Prince liked to hold his infant son in his arms and sing to him. The baby had his father's curly brown hair and his mother's deep blue eyes but everyone said he looked just like his father

which made the Prince prouder still.

The baby gurgled and curled his fingers around his father's. The Prince was delighted. This was the most beautiful baby in the world. He knew his son would grow up strong and fearless. He looked forward to teaching him to ride and taking him on hunting trips.

When the baby was born, Gelert decided that it would be his special responsibility to look after the little Prince. At night, he slept in the nursery at the foot of the cradle. If the baby cried, he ran to wake the Princess, watching anxiously until the child was settled back in his cot.

Gelert had been given to Prince Llewellyn by his aged father. A puppy, so small that the Prince had been able to hold him in the palm of his hand, that nuzzled him with a cold nose and licked his hand with a rough, pink tongue. It had been winter, and

THE STORY OF GELERT

the Prince had slipped the little furry bundle inside his tunic to keep the tiny creature warm.

The Princess had put a basket for him in front of the fire in the Great Hall of the castle but he had soon grown too big for it.

Gelert followed his master everywhere. When the Prince was away, he guarded the Princess.

The happy couple decided to hold a christening party so that everyone could see their son. A list of guests was prepared. There were grandparents, aunts and uncles, nieces and nephews, first, second and third cousins, and lords and ladies. The list grew and grew as the couple added to it. Early each morning, messengers left on horseback to deliver the invitations.

The Princess decided the castle must be cleaned from the top turret to the dungeon. Floors were scrubbed, carpets were brushed and curtains

were washed. The Prince spent much of the time in the nursery away from the hustle and bustle. He had invited people to come and see his son and he thought all this preparation was quite unnecessary.

Gelert too kept out of the way in case anyone decided that he should be bathed.

The baby Prince was to wear the lace christening gown worn by his father but the Princess decided everyone else should have new clothes for the occasion.

Everyone was measured. Silks and satins, velvets and furs were cut and eight seamstresses pleated and pinned and sewed as fast as they could.

The Princess had the tiniest of waists and the blue velvet of her gown matched the colour of her eyes. She brushed her hair as usual and then brushed it again so that it gleamed like spun gold.

Her tiara was made from Welsh gold and glittered with diamonds.

The Prince allowed himself to be measured but found it tedious to stand still. He suggested the seamstress draw around his shadow on the ground and make his suit to fit that. But the young girl only smiled and continued to pin, sew and snip.

At last he could put up with it no longer and shook off the clothes telling the alarmed seamstress to make the clothes any size she liked.

The list of guests was now so long that new furniture had to be made. Carpenters planed and nailed until the Great Hall was full of tables and chairs.

The Prince watched the Princess hurrying by, always with a list in her hand and always counting.

Quickly he returned to the nursery and smiled down at his son, sleeping and blissfully unaware of

the commotion he was causing.

The cooks were busy too. Pies, cakes and preserves filled the larder to overflowing. No one seemed to know exactly how many guests were expected and so they prepared generously.

There were to be twelve courses: ducks, pheasants, chickens and geese, beef and pork pies, salmon and trout, leek and potato soup, honey cake, teisen lap, apple cake and upside down cake, four kinds of tarts and five kinds of bread.

Meat was roasted on spits, cawl simmered in pots, cakes and bread were baked in the oven and on griddles.

Everything was tasted and approved by the Head Cook. He prodded and stirred, tasted and sipped, closed his eyes and considered carefully.

'More pepper.'

'More salt.'

'Simmer gently.'

'Perfect.'

'Just right.'

The Prince had created a special drink from honey and wines and herbs so that everyone could toast the health of his son. It sparkled in a large silver bowl in the centre of a mahogany table. Around the bowl were tiny silver goblets.

The Princess said it was delicious and hoped it was not too strong.

Everyone who was important came to the castle. Some came on horseback and some by carriage. Others sent their servants on ahead to prepare their rooms.

The Prince and Princess greeted their guests and soon the castle was full of excited, laughing, chattering people.

A grand ball was held and the Prince and

THE STORY OF GELERT

Princess led the dancing. All admired the Princess's beauty and said how well they danced together and how the baby would grow up as strong and handsome as his father.

Everyone had brought presents for the baby Prince: a goblet made of Welsh gold, a silver cross, the white fleece of a ewe to keep him warm, a carafe of holy water to bless him.

The baby smiled happily and all the while Gelert kept watch.

At last the party was over. Some of the guests were going with the Prince and Princess to the hunting lodge but it was time for the others to leave. Bags and cases were packed and trunks were fastened and loaded on to carriages.

The Prince and Princess waved goodbye from the gates of the castle and Gelert made sure nothing was left behind.

THE STORY OF GELERT

When the Prince went hunting, Gelert went too, running ahead following secret trails in search of prey, always returning to let the Prince know that all was well.

He barked excitedly when he disturbed an unsuspecting pheasant or rabbit and they always escaped him.

The Prince's hunting lodge nestled in the forest at the foot of Snowdon and lately, Gelert had detected a heavy scent which made him uneasy.

There had been rumours that a large wolf had been sighted near the lodge. The Prince shrugged his shoulders, telling the Princess that Gelert would soon see off any predator who came near.

Gelert knew there was danger but he could not make the Prince understand. He knew he must stay close to the baby Prince at all times.

Gelert inspected all the guests but there was

no trace of the scent which had worried him in the forest. Satisfied that all was well, he returned to his place beside the baby's cot.

An elderly aunt asked if it was safe to allow such a big dog so close to the little Prince.

Prince Llewellyn laughed. 'I would trust Gelert with my life. No harm will come to my son while Gelert is there to guard him.'

He patted Gelert affectionately and the dog wagged his tail with pride.

In the middle of the lodge was a large hall with a long table. At one end of the hall was an open hearth.

The kill from the hunt was cooked on a spit over the open fire, filling the lodge with mouth-watering smells. Gelert stretched out in front of the fire, just out of reach of the fat that sizzled and spluttered as it fell on the red-hot

coals.

The Prince cut a slice of meat with his sword, tasted it and nodded approvingly.

Soon all the guests were seated at the table, eating and congratulating each other on their hunting skills.

Gelert walked around, picking up any unwanted bones and stopping at the Prince's side for the titbits his master always gave him.

At last all had eaten their fill and the guests made their way outside into the late afternoon sunshine.

Gelert stretched out in front of the fire and went to sleep.

The next morning, the lodge was strangely quiet. The servants, usually laughing and chattering were silent and one maid seemed to have been crying.

THE STORY OF GELERT

There were muddy paw marks all over the floor.

As well the bones and meat from the previous day were missing. Cook was angry because he had been going to make soup from them and the maid was upset because the floor was so dirty.

Soon Gelert realised that he was being blamed. The maid wiped her eyes and looked at him reproachfully. Even the Princess was cross with him.

He sniffed the marks and growled deep within his throat, recognising the scent. The wolf had been inside the lodge. Gelert barked, trying to make them understand the danger but no one seemed to understand.

Gelert hurried back to the little Prince and determined not to leave him alone.

After breakfast, the guests went hunting. The Princess decided to join the party leaving the

THE STORY OF GELERT

little Prince in the charge of his nanny.

Gelert wanted to stay behind and look after the baby but Prince Llewellyn called him and obediently, he followed his master.

For a while, Gelert forgot about the wolf as he looked for prey to chase. A butterfly landed on his nose, making him sneeze.

It was a while before he realised what was missing. There was no trace of the evil scent of the wolf. At first he was pleased but then he remembered the paw marks on the floor.

Quickly he turned and ran as fast as he could back to the lodge. The Prince shouted to him to stop but for once, Gelert would not obey.

His throat hurt as he breathed deeply and quickly, fearful that he would be too late.

He caught his paw in brambles but did not stop.

Near the lodge the scent of the wolf was

everywhere. Gelert could hear the little Prince whimpering. Crawling along the floor, the dog pushed open the door.

It was late in the evening before the hunters, tired but happy, returned. The Prince and Princess hurried ahead. The Prince was puzzled by Gelert's behaviour and the Princess was anxious to see her son.

It was dusk and the lodge was full of strange shadows. The Prince called for the nanny but there was no reply.

Then he saw the blood on the wall. He called again and Gelert crawled weakly towards him. The dog's fur was soaked with blood and one leg hung broken and useless.

'You've killed my son,' the Prince cried in horror.

With one swift movement, he raised his sword

and plunged it deep into the dog. Gelert looked sadly at his master and whimpered. Then lay still. He was dead.

The Prince hurried to the nursery. The little Prince's cot was upturned and from beneath it came a tiny cry. Quickly, the Prince bent down and lifted the cradle.

His baby son pushed his arms out of his shawl and raised them to his father. Tenderly, the Prince cradled the child in his arms.

Then he saw the body of the wolf. The Prince realised that the wild animal had come into the lodge and that Gelert had killed it to save the baby Prince.

Silently, he handed the baby to the Princess.

Gently, he withdrew his sword from the dog's body and picked up Gelert. Weeping, he carried Gelert to the place where they had often sat

THE STORY OF GELERT

together in the sun and laid his friend to rest.

He called the place Beddgelert, the Grave of Gelert and marked it with a stone.

The stone still marks the grave of the courageous Gelert today.

© D C and E J Perkins, 1990

ISBN 1 85122 098 4

DOMINO BOOKS LTD., P O Box 78, Swansea SA1 1YT.